The Alternat

an inkling — a miniature fountain pen

The Alternative Dictionary

Michael Johnstone

Illustrated by Ian Dicks

An Armada Original

The Alternative Dictionary was first published in Armada in 1987.

Armada is an imprint of the Children's Division, part of
the Collins Publishing Group, 8 Grafton Street, London W1X 3LA.

© 1987 Michael Johnstone
© illustrations 1987 Ian Dicks

Printed and bound in Great Britain by
William Collins Sons & Co. Ltd, Glasgow

Z

Zeal An enthusiastic sea creature related to the Zea lion.

Zebra crossing Breeding African herbivores with other animals.

Zebrawood Black and white striped animals that branch out all over Africa.

Zero option The choice facing an examiner when faced with an atrocious paper.

Zincography The science of washing up.

Zither One of a pair of musical instruments played by street musicians who play hither and zither.

Zoo A place where animals are barred.

Zoogeography The study of the layouts of wildlife parks.

Zoophobia Fear of zoos.

Zootonomy The book in the Bible that comes between Kings II and Judges.

Zulu A public convenience in a game park.

Zwieback To have one's mind on something other than one is doing. eg. Zwieback and think of England.

Y

Yale lock   A strand of hair cut from the head of an American college graduate.

Yankee Doodle   An American cartoon.

Yankee Doodle Dandy   A well-dressed American cartoonist.

Yardarm   Either of the upper limbs that have reached a length of three feet.

Yard of ale   Three drunken feet.

Yashmak   A phrase often used by drunken Scots. eg. 'Yashmak, I knowsh what you'sh talking about.'

Yawp   *Young, awfully wearisome person.*

Yearbook   A novel that takes an awfully long time to read.

Yearling   A period of between three and six months.

Yellow fever   An attack of cowardice that spreads through a regiment like wildfire.

Yellow line   A file of soldiers who won't fight.

Yellow Pages   Cowardly train-bearers.

Yen   A strong desire to spend Japanese money.

Yes-man   Anyone who is not a real no-no.

Yiddish A piece of crockery belonging to a Hebrew family.

Yours An illness that afflicts alcoholics. eg. 'I've got a bad attack of yours today.' 'What's yours?' 'Thanks very much. Gin and tonic please.'

Youth Something that is wasted on the young.

Youth club A stick used as a weapon by a young layabout.

Yucca An expression of distaste.

Yugoslav A command to a southeastern European to leave.

X

Xerox Stones, as in Xerox of Gibraltar.

XX A double-cross.

W

Waging war   A battle fought between weekly-paid soldiers.

Wake up   Mind over mattress.

Wallaby   An Australian cradle-song.

Waltz   Belonging to or pertaining to Walter.

Ward of court   A hospital room set aside for members of the legal profession.

Warfare   A soldier's daily rations while on active service.

Waspish   How you feel when you have a bee in your bonnet.

Watchstrap   A device for catching errant Timexes.

Water on the brain   A medical condition easily cured by a tap on the brow.

Waterbuck   Awash with money.

Waterfowl   To impede the progress of a swimmer by unfair methods.

Wax lyrical   To polish up your poetry.

Weather wise   Descriptive of meteorologist.

Weaverbird   A flying animal that looms on the horizon.

Webster   An industrious spider.

Wedding ring   A one-man band.

Wedlock   A pre-marital agreement never to get divorced.

Weekday   A day when you are not feeling your strongest.

Weight loss   The triumph of mind over platter.

Well-bred   A sliced loaf that is in tip-top condition.

Well done   A source of oil that has dried up.

Welsh rarebit   Someone in Cardiff with an IQ of over 100.

West   What wabbits do when they get tired wunning about?

Westerlies   The Kremlin view of White House statements.

Wet nurse   An SRN caught in a shower without an umbrella.

Wheel of fortune   A Rolls Royce or any other extremely expensive car.

Wheeler dealer   A second-hand tyre salesman.

Whippet   To attack the budgie with a belt.

Whisky Mac   An indication that one wants to buy a Scotsman a drink.

Whit Sunday   (Scots) An expression used to ascertain the day of the week someone has been talking about. eg. 'Whit Sunday you on aboot?'

White collar worker   A laundress who bleaches and starches shirts.

White elephant stall   Where to buy albino ungulates.

White sauce   A cheeky remark made by a Caucasian.

Wholemeal   Hors d'oeuvre, soup, sorbet, fish, meat, cheese, fruit, pudding, coffee and brandy.

Wild oats   Carefree sow and sows.

Wildcat strike   An attack by a mad mog.

Willpower   The ability to impose one's wishes on one's relatives after one has died.

Wine cooler   A prison for alcoholics.

Wing chair   A flying sofa.

Winning post   A mail delivery that brings news of success in the football pools.

Winsome . . .   . . . (and you) lose some.

Wire-haired terrier   A dog that is useful for cleaning pots and pans.

Wire wool   1. An SOS from an avid knitter.   2. Fibre necessary for cable stitching.

Wisecracks   A hole in the wall that gets bigger by degrees.

Wisteria   A place in which to be wistful.

Withershins   The way in which an enthusiastic hockey player attacks an opponent.

Wit's end   The death of a comedian.

Witchcraft   A flying broomstick.

Wolf in sheep's clothing   Glutton dressed as lamb.

Wolf-hound   A dog that eats too quickly.

Wolf whistle   A piercing noise made by wild dogs.

Wombat   An Australian vampire.

Wood pigeon   A carved bird.

Woodwork teacher   A chip off the old block.

Woolly-headed   Having a purly complexion but a plain face.

Work   The curse of the drinking classes.

Wrong side of the law   A policeman with appendicitis.

Wrestling match   A bellicose device for making fire.

Wrist band   A group of pianists.

Wrong number   What you always get when you use your last ten pence to make a phone call.

Wunderbar   A pub for dreamers.

V

Vacuum cleaner   1. A collective noun.   2. A proper sucker.

Vampire   Someone who loves in vein.

Vanish   Having the appearance of a small lorry.

Vanishing cream   Descriptive of a carton of cream in a kitchen in which there is only a cat.

Varnished   Disappeared in a new, shiny coat.

Vat 69   The Pope's telephone number.

Vertigo   A problem that faces tourists on a rainy day. eg. Vertigo today?

Vespers   A very quietly sung religious service.

Vice versa   Smutty Italian poetry.

Vicious circle.   A round shape with a bad temper.

Viking   The sixth male monarch in any dynasty.

View-finder   A paid tourist guide.

Vindictive   Wine that wants to get its own back on you.

Violinist   A dishonest musician who is always on the fiddle.

Viper   A poisonous snake that cleans the windscreen in your car.

Visages   Six wise men.

Vociferous   Having a steely-toned voice.

Volts   To dance in an electrified fashion.
Voluntary liquidation   Having committed suicide by jumping in the Thames.
Vulgarize   To wear too much mascara.

U

Umpire   The judge in a singing competition.
Unabashed   A boxer who leaves the ring undefeated.
Unaccountable   Any sum that is too hard for you to do.
Unallay   A floor covering that goes between the boards and the carpet.
Unaltered   Descriptive of an unmarried person.
Unaware   Clothes worn beneath over-garments.
Unbolted   Food eaten in a leisurely manner.
Unbridled   A man who has been jilted at the altar.
Uncharted   A record that fails to get into the top 50.
Underbred   The place to look for flour weevils.
Underground garage   Wall-to-wall car pit.

Undergrowth   Hair that grows on the soles of your feet.
Undermanned   Descriptive of a dance where there are too many women.

Undermine   (German) A stoat with its winter coat.

Underpants   Breathes less heavily than expected.

Underrate   Consumed less than the host or hostess had catered for.

Underwrite   To make marks on the obverse side of a piece of paper.

Union Jack   A sailor who belongs to a trade union.

Unit   A term of abuse.

Unprincipled   A school where the headmaster has been fired.

Unseasonable   To be without salt, pepper or herbs.

Unsuitable   To be too fat to get into last years' clothes.

Unsuited   Naked.

Untapped   Descriptive of a virgin shoulder.

Uphill struggle   A dispute between nations for the ownership of a mountain.

Upsy-daisy   A socially-mobile flower.

Upwards   Hospital rooms where the patients are feeling just dandy.

Urban guerilla   A primate that lives in London Zoo.

Urchin   The lower part of a woman's face.

Useless sucker   A defunct vacuum cleaner.

T

Table d'hôte   The place to eat a hot snack.

- **Tablet**   A small table.
- **Tail wagging**   A happy ending.
- **Take the rap**   To hang up one's wife's shawl.
- **Tangent**   A man who has been in the sun too long.

Tank regiment   Fish with military training.

Tap dancing   Moving to music that gives one a sinking feeling.

Tarmacadam   An expression of gratitude used when talking to the first Scotsman.

Tea trolley   Meals on wheels.

- **Team spirit**   A bottle of Scotch placed in the dressing room for the victorious side of a sporting contest to enjoy.

Telephone kiosk   A yak in the box.

Tempis fugit   (Latin) The girl from the Brook Street Bureau has left already.

Tennis   The answer to the question 'what is the number between nine and eleven?'

- **Tennis racket**   A tennis tournament organized by the Mafia.

RAT-A-TAT!
TAT-TAT!

Tequilla   The Gulp of Mexico.

Termites   Very boring insects.

Test Act   To audition for a stage role.

Test pilot   Someone who hopes to pass an exam with flying colours.

Thick-skinned   Descriptive of a sausage that defies knife and fork.

Think tank   An armoured fighting vehicle with a mind of its own.

Thongs   What thingers thing.

Tibet   A country full of gamblers.

Timpani   The centre of the music business – Timpani Alley.

Toadstool   A small chair for frogs.

Toboggan   The reason why one attends an auction.

Toilet water   Something you dab on the skin when you're feeling flushed.

Tomorrow   A labour-saving device for today.

Tongue sandwich   Food that keeps repeating itself.

Toodleloo   To bid farewell before locking oneself in the lavatory for a long time.

Toothcomb   A grooming device for the teeth.

Track suit   To search for a piece of clothing.

Traffic jam   Preserved Datsun Cherries.

Traffic lights   A road-safety device that stops your car whenever you approach them.

Transmogrify   To change a cat into another animal.

Transparent   One or other of the Invisible Man's parents.

Transplant surgeon   A man after your own heart.

Trapeze artist   Someone who needs the gift of the grab.

Travelling circus   A tour de farce.

Treason   (Irish) The explanation.

Trick photography   A lot of focus pocus.

Trigger happy   Roy Rogers' horse while at play.

Triplet   A slight stumble.

Trouble brewing   A storm in a teacup.

Trunk call   An elephant on the telephone.

Tuning fork   A musical companion for someone who plays the spoons.

Turf accountant   A man who makes his living by knowing betters.

Turncoat   A reversible jacket.

TVam A popular breakfast cereal.

Twaddle To walk in a peculiar manner.

Tweak To have insufficient strength to move.

Twilight To attempt to stwike a match.

Twin-engined Powered by Romulus and Remus.

Twirly Any time before 7.30 am.

Twit Part of an owl's song: *twit twoo*.

Twitch A nervous sorceress.

Two thirty The condition of the people found in a Chinese dentist's waiting room.

Ty*coon* A businessman who makes his living by selling neckware.

Tyrant A despotic insect.

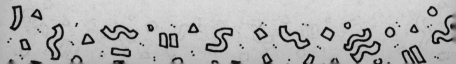

S

Samson   A Biblical character who brought the house down.

Sand grouse   To complain about a beach picnic.

Sardine   The daughter of a Russian ruler.

Saudi Arabia   The home of Islamic pigs.

Scabbard   A playwright who refuses to come out on strike.

Scarcity   What King Kong did to New York.

Scarlet woman   A female revolutionary.

Scenic   To observe a thief at work.

Schizophrenic   Someone who can't make up his minds.

Schnapps   What mum does when she's tired.

Science fiction   A doctored lab-book.

Scholastic   A stretchable material used by learning establishments to keep their standards up.

School teacher   A person who instructs a group of whales.

Scurf   Chips off the old block.

Sealyham   A pig that smells of fish.

Seashell   A bomb fired from a boat.

Second-hand car   An automobile in first-crash condition.

Self-esteem The vapour you breathe out on a frosty night.

Self-raising Someone who walks with a spring in his heels.

Self-service To give yourself the once over.

Sell out A mass escape from prison.

Semi-colon What's left inside a patient after the surgeon has completed a partial colostomy.

Sentimental Despatched a lunatic by post.

Sex The jute bags in which coal is still delivered in polite parts of Glasgow.

Shampoo An imitation of the bear created by A. A. Milne.

Shamrock An imitation diamond.

Shareholder A medieval ploughman.

Sharp-tongued Having the capacity to make cutting remarks.

Shiftless Descriptive of a girl who sleeps in the nude.

Shoplifter A terrorist who blows up Marks and Spencer.

Shoplifting Trouble in store.

Shoulder blade A knife used to carve particular joints of meat.

Sidewards   Hospital rooms for those with appendicitis.

Sikh   An Indian with an upset stomach.

Silver collection   A group of the Lone Ranger's horses.

Simpleton   A heavy weight that's easy to bear.

Sitar   Someone who looks after Indian babies.

Skeleton   An acute case of dieting.

Sleeping pill   An aspirin enjoying forty winks.

Slippery   A shoe cupboard.

Sloe gin   Not the best thing if you want a quick drink.

Small-minded   Someone who thinks about women's underwear a lot.

Smoked fish   A kipper with a fag in its mouth.

Smother   An overprotective female parent.

Snap judgment   The result of a photographic competition.

Sneeze   The bones halfway up your legs.

Snore   To sleep soundly.

Soporific   Descriptive of a fantastic mop.

Soprano   A murderess on the high Cs.

Sorceress   A cook who is over-generous with the tomato ketchup.

Sour puss   A cat that's just sucked a lemon.

Soviet A Russian napkin.
Spanish fly The zip on a Spaniard's trousers.
Spectacles Sight for sore eyes.
Spell-binding B . .I . .N . .D . .I . . N . .G
Spice The plural of spouse.

Spin bowler A cricket-playing spider.
Spit roast Meat that's done to a turn.
Split second A dead-heat for runner-up in a race.
Spring chicken A bird with elastic legs.
Spring lamb A young sheep with rubber legs.
Square-bashing Attacking a rectangle with four equal sides.
Square meal A round of sandwiches that can be had up under the Trade Description Act.
Stalactite What goes down . . .
Stalagmite . . . Must come up.
Standing order A command to get up.
Starfish A successful stage-struck sea creature.
Starry-eyed Descriptive of an astronomer.
Stay of execution To keep one's head when all around are losing theirs.
Sting in the tail Remarks made by those with a waspish sense of humour.

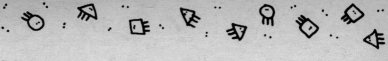

Sub-committee The men and women who meet regularly to inspect underwater ships.

Suicide To kill everyone called Susan.

Summit conference A meeting of world leaders held on Mount Everest.

Sunbathing An a-peeling way to pass the time.

Sunburn To get more than you bask for.

Sunburnt Descriptive of a well-red person.

Surgeon Medical man who is cut out for what he does.

Suspended animation Just hanging around for a long time.

Swan song A cygneture tune.

Sweepstakes Lotteries held by chimney cleaners.

G-R-R-R-!

PERKINS PIG FARM NEW E.E.C. HYGIENE RULES

Sweet and sour pork A perfumed, ill-tempered pig.

Swimming baths A bidet doing the breast stroke.

Swimming trunks Two elephants splashing about in the water.

Swine fever A disease you get from drinking too much swine.

R

Rabid   What Scottish auctioneers hope that those attending their sales will do.

Racketeer   A dishonest tennis player.

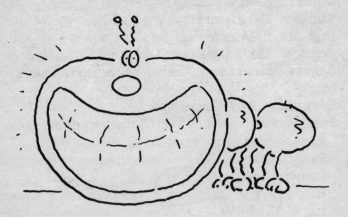

Radiant   A cheerful insect.

Radio ham   A pig with a two-way transmitter.

Radio telescope   A magnifying device that assists users to locate distant wirelesses.

Ragtime   Cinderella after midnight.

Raining cats and dogs   A heavy shower that results in poodles on the pavement.

Rainproof   Evidence that there has been recent precipitation.

Raising Cain   Growing sugar.

Rake's progress   The rate at which the lawn is cleared of autumn leaves.

Ram   A non-ewe sheep.

Rampart   A non-ewe divorce.

Ramshackle   To tie up a male sheep.

Rash decision   (Medical) A diagnosis of measles, acne or one of several skin diseases.

Raven-haired   Having a headful of blackbirds.

Raving beauties   Beauty contest runners-up when the least attractive contestant has won.

Rear admiral   A naval officer who commands from the back.

Rebate   To put another worm on the hook.

Rebelling   Ringing again.

Rebore   To tell the same joke over and over again.

Rebuff   To clean your nails again.

Reckless   An accident-prone person on a good day.

Red admiral   A senior officer in the Russian navy.

Red-letter day   When people in Moscow get their mail.

Redolent   Of or pertaining to unemployment benefit.

Refined oil   Liquid carbon that comes out of the ground in the best possible taste.

Regicide   To kill all those called Reginald.

Registration number   Something to take when you feel run down.

Relent   Something that's borrowed again and again.

Repealed   Rang the church bells more than once.

Research   To plagiarize from more than one source.

Reservations What rich people make for lunch and dinner.

Respects Of or pertaining to a pair of glasses.

Restitution A home for those suffering from a nervous breakdown.

Revolving door The place to meet the girl you're going around with.

Rhubarb To regret the cynical comment one has just made.

Riplet A small tear.

Road hog A pig of a driver.

Roadsweeper A brush with the law.

Rock festival A convention for geologists.

Rookery Any shop with over-inflated prices.

Rough idea Where a golfer thinks his ball is.

Round dozen Twelve doughnuts.

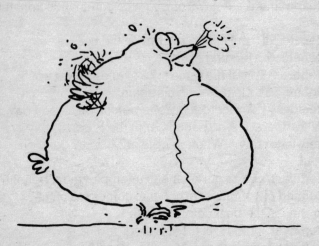

Round robin A bird that needs to go on a diet.

Rugby A game for barbarians played by gentlemen.

Rule of thumb What Tom says, goes.

Q

Quack An unqualified vet who specializes in treating sick water birds.
Quadrille A very square dance.
Quadruplets Four crying out loud.
Quartz What there are four of in a gallon.
Queen's guide A dog that leads blind monarchs.
Question master The smart alec who knows all the answers.
Quick-change artist A very fast bank clerk.
Quincentenary A pear-shaped, Asian fruit's tenth birthday.

P

Padded cell A battery in an anorak.
Paddy field The place for growing Irishmen.
Palette A small chum.
Palette knife The instrument with which a surgeon operates on the roof of the mouth.
Palm tree A plant that grows on the front of your hand.

Panther Thomone who hath jutht run a long rathe.

Papal bull A load of rubbish issued by the Vatican.

Parachuting A popular sport with drop-outs.

Paramedic A Red Devil with a degree in surgery.

Parameter A device for measuring the length of paragraphs.

Parasite A citizen of the capital of France.

Parental An agency that provides temporary fathers.

Parricide The murder of young salmon.

Pas de deux 1. (French) Father of twins. 2. (Irish – pronounced Paddy Doo) A dove.

Passé (French) Indicative that father has just remarked on something.

Passing fancy A cake on a dessert trolley.

Passion play A theatrical performance from which under-eighteen-year-olds are banned.

Past perfect Having a spotless record.

Pasturage Being older than the person one is talking to.

Patagonia An announcement that pater has left mater.

Pattern The father of a young sea bird.

Pauper The man who married your mother.

Peashooter A pea's nose.

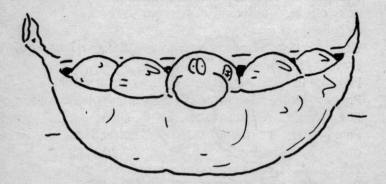

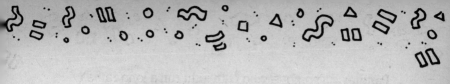

Peccadillo 1. A chicken on an armadillo's back.
2. A street in London that runs from Green Park to Peccadillo Circus.

Pedant A very dull insect.

Pedestrian 1. Someone who should be seen and not hurt. 2. A motorist who has found somewhere to park.

Peer group A gathering of short-sighted people.

Pelting down A shower of feathers.

Pen pals Two pigs having an affair.

Peppermint A Polo with the hole filled in.

Perforations Legalized rip-offs.

Petty officer A seaman in charge of very minor matters.

Philanthropist Someone who cannot decide if he is in love with Phil or Ann.

Philisophic The reason why Philip is not at school.

Phoney Someone who makes misleading phone calls.

Photocopier A visual plagiarizer.

Photo-finish 1. The end of a reel of film. 2. A graduation picture.

Photoflash Indecent exposure.

Physiology The study of lemonade.

Picnicker   Someone who steals digging implements.

Pigeon-toed   Descriptive of a carriage pulled by birds.

Piggy bank   The place to save your bacon.

Pig-headed   Having a swine of a cold.

Pig ignorant   Totally lacking in sty-le.

Pikestaff   A fish weapon.

Pillage   The age you are when you cannot get to sleep without a mogadon.

Pin money   An acupuncturist's fee.

Pious   A meal eaten during Lent. eg. steak and kidney pious, shepherd's pious.

Pipe dreams   What organists have when they sleep.

Pizza   Part of.

Plain singing   Singing a dull song.

Plain speaking   Talking about aeroplanes.

Plastic Mac   A transparent Scotsman.

Plastic surgeon   A medically qualified man who melts if he gets too warm.

Plastic surgery   To effect a repair on any of several synthetic materials with a polymeric structure.

Poached egg   A thief's breakfast.

Pocket calculator   A machine for counting trouser pockets.

Pole position   Somewhere between East Germany and USSR.

Polyandrous   To be married to a parrot.
Polygamy   A parrot with a broken leg.

Polyglot   A speech impediment that afflicts parrots.
Polygon   A dead parrot.
Polymeric   Descriptive of a parrot from the United States.
Polyphony   A budgie that poses as a parrot.
Polyunsaturated fat   An obese, dry parrot.
Pomme de terre   (Australian) A dead Englishman.
Pop art   Coca Cola advertisement.
Pop singer   Someone who appears in Coca Cola advertisements.
Population   The worship of Rice Krispies.
Portal   A shelter. eg. In a storm any portal do.
Portuguese   A flock of water birds from the Algarve.
Positive   A proper no-no.
Possess   To own a lavatory.
Post mark   To mail a unit of German currency.
Pot luck   An unidentified cooking object.
Pot roast   Sunburn on the stomach.
Poverty   Watching the world go buy.
Pragmatic   A gun made in the capital of Czechoslovakia.
Precursor   Someone who is too young to know any bad language.

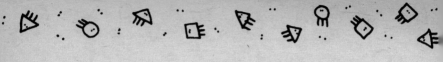

Predator An ex-boy friend who follows you around.

Predestination The stop before you get off.

Perfect An over-zealous authoritarian, until you become one yourself.

Pregnant An insect that's expecting a baby.

Pressing engagement A date with a dry cleaner.

Primate A bigamist's first wife.

Primrose A very proper flower.

Prior approval A dispensation that allows priests to marry.

Procure To be in favour of medical treatment.

Profile To be in favour of queuing.

Psychiatrist A Freud egg-head.

Psychopath Crazy paving.

Public eyesore A massive sty that affects more than one person.

Puff adder A cigarette-smoking snake.

Puffin A bird that's always out of breath.

Purgatory To get rid of someone who voted for Mrs Thatcher.

Purse lipped Having put one's money where one's mouth is.

Pusillanimous A meek cat.

Pustular A cat with lots of boils.

Pyromaniac Someone who is addicted to Indian funerals.

O

Oboe (US) A musical tramp.

Octopus A cat with eight legs.

Oddball A dance for eccentrics.

Offal Really bad meat.

Off-peak electricity A power station situated in a valley.

Olé An exhortation used by Spanish farmers to encourage their chickens to produce eggs.

Olefactory The buildings wherein Spanish farmers tell their chickens to get cracking.

One-man band 1. A piece of elastic that holds up trousers. 2. A self-conducting musician.

Ornamental A decorative lunatic.

Out cold Being caught naked in a snowstorm.

Outdo An unfashionable party.

Overbearing Taking off too many clothes.

Over-censored Abridged too far.

Overdraft The state of your bank account when there is too much month at the end of your money.

Over-perfumed Descriptive of someone who has made a fragrant error.

Overweight   The survival of the fat.

Oxfam   A charity that raises money for starving oxen.

Oxymoron   An imbecilic cow.

Oyster   A request to lift your baby sister out of her pram.

N

Nail-biting finish   The cuticles.

Naked truth   1. The bare facts.   2. Descriptive of a nudist taking a lie-detector test.

Narrow-minded   Having tunnel vision.

National Elf Service   Conscription for gnomes.

Naturalized   Descriptive of someone with 20/20 vision.

Navy blue   The state of the senior service when depressed.

Nectarine   A vampire's favourite food.

Negligent   A man who dresses up in a female's night attire.

Neighbour   The people who live next door who knock on the wall when you play your hi-fi just loud enough for you to hear.

Neighbourhood watch   A communal timepiece.

Net   A collection of holes held together by string.

Net result   The outcome of a fishing competition.

Neurosis   The first blooms of a newly-planted rose bush.

New Scotland Yard   0.8 metres.

Nightjar   A drink taken after 6.00 pm.

Nodding acquaintance   A friend who suffers from the shakes.

Nomadic   A wandering elf.

Nosper   A crazy, mixed up person.

Nostalgia   Something that's not what it used to be.

Nothing   A peeled balloon.

Nuclear fission   Using atomic maggots as bait.

Nutcracker Suite   A squirrel's hotel room.

Nuthatch   A squirrel that thinks it's a chicken.

M

Maccabees   Scottish honey makers.

Macramé   A Scottish male sheep.

Magnanimous   A very generous rodent.

Magpie   Mrs Thatcher's favourite pudding.

Majority   What you are never in when things are put to the vote.

Making a spectacle of oneself   Turning into a pair of glasses.

Making ends meet   A dog running round in circles.

Mal de mer   A bug you can catch from your mother.

Mammory   1. Something for which we are all grateful, hence Thanks for the Mammory.   2. A home for tired mams.

Mandrake   An animal that's half human, half duck.

Mandate   A male escort.

Man-handle   A device for picking up men.

Man of many parts   A male who has undergone several transplant operations.

Man overboard   A drip in the ocean.

Marionette   The daughter of a woman called Marion who is also called Marion.

Marmalade   Descriptive of a table laid by your mother.

Massacre   A large area set aside for religious services.

Mass exodus.   A stampede out of church.

Mass suicide   To kill oneself in church.

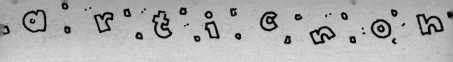

Masterful   Descriptive of a school teacher after lunch.

May   A girl who can't make up her mind.

Mayonnaise   Optical orbs that have seen the glory of the coming of the Lord.

Meal ticket   A luncheon voucher.

Mealy-mouthed   The condition one is in after eating too much porridge.

Mecca   Where followers of Islam hope to die, hence prepare to meet thy Mecca.

Mede   A drink that doesn't suit all tastes – one man's mede is another man's poison.

Medieval   Half bad.

Melancholy   1. A very sad sheepdog.   2. A dog that eats nothing but cantaloupes.

Metronome   A dwarf on the Paris underground.

Mews   Catty remarks.

Mews cottage   A home for abandoned cats.

Microbiologist   A midget scientist.

Microfiche   A very small sea animal.

Microwave   An almost imperceptible movement of the hand.

Middle-aged spread   Butter or margarine that's past its best.

Midwife   The second spouse of a thrice-married man.

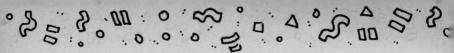

Military coup (Scots) A political animal.

Milk shake A cow with the shivers.

Millionaire Someone who will never go bald.

Mine host Someone who throws underground parties.

Minimum A three-feet high mother.

Minimize To write music in very small notes.

Miniscule A small learning establishment.

Minnehaha A quick giggle.

Mint condition How a Polo should be when you put it in your mouth.

Miscalculation A female arithmetic teacher.

Mischief An Indian leader's daughter.

Misconduct A female band leader.

Miser Someone who lives in poverty so that he can die rich.

Misgiving A generous spinster.

Misinterpret A female translator.

Misrepresentation A female travelling salesperson.

Missing links Stolen sausages.

Missionary Someone who gives cannibals a taste for Christianity.

Misspell A trainee witch.

Mistake A female kleptomaniac.

Mistress To rue the haircut that one has just had.

Mock Tudor   To make fun of Queen Elizabeth I.

Modelling   A pose by any other name.

Mole   A friend of the Earth.

Monkey business   An office run by chimpanzees.

Monk's habit   Something that is surplice to requirements.

Monocle   One on the eye for a lazy pupil.

Monopolies Commission   The government body that has the monopoly in investigating monopolies.

Monotony   Having only one wife at a time.

Monsoon   Who and when a Scottish spinster hopes to meet.

Moose   A Scottish rodent.

Moral philosophy   Ought-to suggestion.

Moral victory   Mrs Whitehouse's aim in life.

Motel   William's sister.

Moth   Thomthing that rolling thtones don't gather.

Mouthful   To be fed up to the back teeth.

Movie buff   Someone who watches films in the nude.

Multi-millionaire   Someone who owns one million multis.

Mushroom   The school dining hall.

Myth   A spinster who talks with a lisp.

L

Labour Day   A public holiday in USA and Canada in honour of those who have suffered the pangs of childbirth.

Labours of Hercules   The pain experienced by Hercules' mother when giving birth.

Labour Party   A social gathering attended by heavily-pregnant women.

Laburnum   A burned-out room in which scientific experiments were held.

Lackadaisical   Being without flowers on the lawn.

Lactic   Being free of insects.

Lactose   Having nothing at the end of your feet.

Lady bountiful   A woman who has eaten too many coconut-filled chocolate bars.

Lagoon   Any of Harry Secombe, Peter Sellers or Spike Milligan.

Laissez-faire   (French) An indolent supernatural being.

Lambaste   To cook a young sheep.

Lambent   Descriptive of a dishonest young sheep.

Lame duck   A water fowl with a broken leg.

Lame excuse   A plea for pardon that can't stand up in court.

Lamprey   Food hunted by young sheep.

Land mine   A claim of ownership of an acre or two.

Land rover   A dog that hates the water.

Lapse   The space between the hip and the knee formed when sitting.

Large scale   Descriptive of an enormous fish.

Largesse   A capital s.

Lassitude   An easy-going dog star.

Last resort   The final count in a general election.

Latest   A French exam.

Laughing stock   Soup with a bubbling sense of humour.

Laundromat   Where keen gardeners take their grass seeds to be washed before planting.

Lavatory   A room with a loo.

Lavender   (French) Someone who sells something.

Lawsuit   An article of clothing worn by members of the legal profession.

Lay preacher   A vicar who stays in bed a lot.

Leading question   Shall we dance . . . ?

Leap year   A kangaroo's birthday.

Legacy   The sport of walking.
Legal eagle   A bird that tries its prey before sentencing it to death.
Legalize   What lawyers tell in truth.

Lemming   A fruit that jumps off cliffs with others of its species.
Lemon   An orange with hepatitis.
Lemonade   A concert organized by Bob Geldof to raise money for citrus fruit farmers.
Leotard   An unpunctual lion.
Lesson   Descriptive of a strip-tease artist at the end of her act.
Letter of the law   A summons to appear in court.
Liable   The capacity to tell untruths.
Liability   Having the capacity to tell untruths.
Liberal Party   A social gathering where anything goes.
Light bulb   A corm that grows lights.
Light-headed   Descriptive of someone who has just had an illuminating idea.
Lightning conductor   A very fast band leader.
Lily-livered   Descriptive of the internal organs of someone in the flower of youth.
Limerick   A good rhyme had by all.
Linden   A tree that shouldn't be washed in public.

Lisp   When you call a spade a thpade.

Listless   Having left the shopping list at home.

Listed building   The Leaning Tower of Pisa.

Literacy   The act of scattering litter.

Litre   A family of metric pups.

Live   Something you only do once. Get it right and it's enough. Get it wrong and it seems to last forever.

Livelihood   An active gangster.

Liverpool   A store of organs ripe for transplant surgery.

Loan shark   A fish with an interest in what everyone else does.

Lobster   A tennis-playing shellfish.

Locate   How one greets girls called Kate.

Loo roll   A sandwich filled with absorbent paper.

Look daggers   Being very sharp-eyed.

Loudspeaker   Someone who is constantly told to 'Shh' in a library.

Lorgnette   A small patch of cultivated grass.

Lorry   Something that fell off the back of a ferry.

Lunatic   An astronaut's watch.

Lynching   Trial by fury.

K

Kaftan Descriptive of girls called Katherine who have been in the sun.

Karma The automobile driven by your mother.

Kayak Something an Eskimo can't have and eat at the same time.

Kernel 1. Where to keep a nutty dog. 2. The nut who ranks below Brigadier.

TONK! TINK!

Kettle drummer A musician who plays kettles.

Keyhole A very important opening.

Key ring An important telephone call.

Kidnapping Descriptive of a young goat having a snooze.

Kidneys The legs of a young goat.

Kill-joy What the Beverley twins would like to do to their elder sister.

Kindred Inborn fear of one's relations.

Kipling Twenty winks.

Kit bag A sack for carrying young cats.

Knackery A place to learn some skills.

Knapsack A sleeping bag.

Knee joint A meeting place for knees.

Knobs   Objects of a-door-ation.

Knockout punch   A very strong mixed drink.

Knotty problem   Something that faces those who find it difficult to unwind.

Knuckle down   The feathers that grow on the back of the hand.

Kosher   To attack a woman in accordance with Jewish laws.

Krone   A very old Danish woman.

Ku Klux Klan   A Scottish cow that sounds like a chicken.

Kumquat   Inevitable, as in kumquat may.

J

Jack   A man with a car on his head.

Jacuzzi   The social whirl.

Jalousie   Blind passion.

Jam session   A weekly meeting of the Women's Institute.

Jargon   Descriptive of an empty store cupboard.

Jasmine   How a German proposes to his girlfriend.

Jerry-built   Constructed in Germany.

Jet set   An aeroplane that has crashed into wet concrete.

Jet setter   A dog that travels in Concorde.

Job centre   A place where those with nothing to do go to be told that there is nothing for them to do.

Joint account   A deposit in a bank used by drug addicts who withdraw from it to pay for their cigarettes.

Jubilant   A queen insect who has reigned for fifty years.

Judicious   The plates off which Hebrews eat their meals.

Juicy   A question asked to verify what one has just witnessed. eg. 'Juicy what I see.'

July   Accusing someone of being mendacious.

Jumbo burger   An elephant on a toasted bun.

Jumbo jet   A flying elephant.

Jumper   An article of clothing you are told to put on when your mother feels cold.

Junk food   Meals served on Chinese ships.

Juno   A Roman goddess who hosted *Mastermind*.

I

I Spy Book A Peeping Tome.
Idiot Someone who lives in a densely populated city.
Igloo An Eskimo's lavatory.
Illegal A bird that does not enjoy good health.
Impact An announcement that one is ready to go on holiday.
Impale A claim that one is feeling unwell.

Impeccable Unable to be eaten by a bird.
Important A foreign insect.
Impregnable Barren: unable to conceive.
Improper A claim that one has been very well brought up.
In Arcadia Ego Words used by a fruit machine addict.
Incense Fashionable perfumes.
Incessant An insect that won't give up.
Incest The thing that many a true word is said in.
In cold blood The manner in which a rare steak is served in a bad restaurant.
Incurable A pig that's too old to eat.
Indentures Fashionable false teeth.
In depth interview A conversation between two or more people held at the shallow end of a swimming pool.

In-fighting   A fashionable boxing match.

Inflammatory   Descriptive of a desire to set fire to Mrs Thatcher.

Inflated opinion   A balloon with a mind of its own.

Ingenious   A very fashionable guy with an IQ of 200.

Inkling   A young pen.

Insane   Parisians, when swimming.

Insanity   A hereditary disease you get from your children.

Insider dealing   A bridge game in Pentonville.

Intermission   Descriptive of a Jesuit priest between jobs.

Investment   Money put into underwear.

Iron rations   Food for those with a taste for steel.

Ivory tower   An elephant's grave yard.

Ivy   A blooming nuisance.

H

Habit-forming   Making nuns' clothes.

Hacking cough   A throat irritation that affects huntsmen.

Haggard   Someone who rides shotgun on a witch's broomstick.

Haggle   A gathering of witches.

Haircut   A clip around the ears.

Hair do   A party for rabbits.

Hair-raising   Rabbit forming.

Hair salon   The place where women go to curl up and dye.

Half-buried   What happens to those who feel half dead.

Half-hitch   A small snag.

Half-hunter   An immature steeplechaser.

Half measure   What you can do with a three-feet ruler to a six-feet length.

Half-past   Descriptive of someone who is at death's door.

Halftime   What you wish the history master would do to his lessons.

Halfwit   Cannon without Ball.

Ham sandwich   Food that acts badly on you.

Handbook   A palmistry manual.

Handicap   A convenient piece of headgear.

Handicraft   A convenient ship.

Happy medium   A cheerful spiritualist.

Hard-headed   Descriptive of the Man in the Iron Mask.

Hard-hearted   A medical condition: the result of having one's blood frozen.

Hardship   A sailing vessel built of steel.

Hardware   An overstarched shirt.
Harebell   1. A beautiful rabbit.   2. A wig that rings.
Hatchback car   A mobile battery farm.
Hay fever   An illness that affects grass widows.
Head boy   A scholar who is usually in good form.
Headshrinker   The manageress of a dry cleaning shop.
Heatstroke   How to get out of hot water.
Heavy Metal Music   An iron band.
Hebrew   Men-only beer.
Hedgehog   A pig that won't make up its mind.
Heirloom   A machine for weaving heirs.
Heir presumptive   How a bald man feels on entering a wig shop.
Hermit   A woman's glove.
Hermit crab   A mollusc that won't talk to anyone.
Hero   Someone who, like tight shoes, never admits defeat.
Herods   A dynasty of Egyptian rulers who founded the top-people's store.
Heroic couplet   Romeo and Juliet.
Heroine addict   Someone who is always reading Mills and Boon paperback romances.

Hexachord Agreement between witches.

Hexagram The method used by witches to send spells to each other.

Hexameter A machine that measures the power of spells.

Highball A dance held on top of the Empire State Building.

Highchair A friendly greeting to a seat.

High-handed The result of having one's arms in plaster.

High tea The note below top c.

High time Midnight on top of Mount Everest.

Highland fling Tossing the caber.

Highland Light Infantry The Scottish Electricity Board.

Highly strung A violin lying on top of the Empire State Building.

Hillbilly A goat living on the top of Mount Everest.

Himalaya A very confused Italian cockerel.

Hindsight Looking at life through doe eyes.

Hip bone Something a trendy dog chews on.

Hippodrome Where to catch a flying hippopotamus.

Hippy The bonies at the top of the leggies.

Historian Someone who refuses to let bygones be bygones.

History The tale of a man.

Hogwash A pig's laundry.

Hollow An empty greeting.

Hollyhocks A plant that pawns itself.

Holy Ghost A bible-carrying spook.

Holy Murder The Crucifixion.

Holy Orders The word of God.

Home economics Living on a budget.

Homework Schoolwork usually completed on the bus.

Honeycomb A sticky contraption for untangling hair.

Hootenanny The offspring of an owl and a goat.

Hot and cold in every room A contradiction of terms.

Hot cross bun An angry cake with a high temperature.

Hot-headed Descriptive of someone whose hair is on fire.

Humbug A smelly fly.

Humdinger A cross between a bee and the belle of the ball.

Hunting horn Riding out in search of a unicorn.

Hydrogen bomb Something that makes molehills out of mountains.

Hygiene The way to greet girls called Jean.

Hypochondria Someone who is allergic to good health.

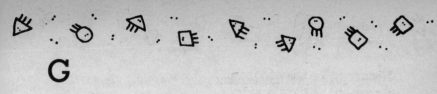

G

Gallows   Not the place to be found hanging around.

Game bird   A female old age pensioner at a disco.

Garibaldi   Anyone called Gary who is suffering from alopecia.

Garter snake   A reptile that snaps on occasion.

Gas bill   Something that makes your father thermally ill.

Gastric   The manner in which a magician lights his cooker.

Gastronome   1. A fairy-tale character with his head in the oven.   2. An elf with a well-developed palate.

Gegs   Scrambled eggs.

General anaesthetic   A sleeping pill used by military leaders.

General assembly   A meeting between the leaders of the army and senior officers in the Salvation Army.

General election   The process by which senior army officers are selected.

Geriatric   A Berlin conjurer.

Germicide   A virus that kills itself.

Giraffe   An animal that's head and shoulders above the others.

Glamorize   To wear sequined eye-shadow.

Gnu An animal that is mistrusted by many, hence the expression, 'no gnus is good gnus'.

Goat A rude animal that always butts in.

Goatskin Related to a goat.

Goblet (Scots) A small opening between the nose and the chin.

Goblin An elf that bolts its food.

Godsend A statue of Buddha that has just been smashed.

Gold digger A sunburnt Australian.

Goldfish To angle in vein.

Golf A good walk spoiled.

Goodwill The manner in which an inheritor views the last wishes of his benefactor.

Gooseberry A bird in the bush.

Gorgeous To have the appearance of a deep ravine.

Gospel A command from a witch teacher to her pupils.

Gossips People who let the chat out of the bag.

Gotten To achieve 10% in an exam.

Goulash A stew eaten by ghosts.

Gramophone A very light Irish record player.

Granary A home for old ladies.

Grand prix A very large rose bush.

Grandee A capital e.

Grand slam   A great boxing match.

Granite   A dwarf's grandmother.

Graniteware   The clothes worn by granites.

Granny annex   To take over your mum's mum.

Granny flat   The outcome of an accident involving a grandmother and a steam roller.

Grapeshot   Mulled wine.

Grave issue   A dispute over burial rights.

Gravely ill   Someone suffering from mourning sickness.

Grave mistake   A confusion over a corpse's identity.

Graveyard   Three very depressed feet.

Gravity   The study of burial places.

Gravy train   The packet of Bisto arriving at Platform 10.

Green-fingered   Descriptive of a punk wearing nail varnish.

Grilled trout   A fish that's been questioned by the police.

Grim death   The demise of one or other of a pair of story-telling brothers.

Groundless   1. Very weak coffee.   2. Descriptive of a soccer player who has been on the transfer list for ten years.

Groundsheet   The temperature of the pavement.

Growing pains   An ache that gets worse and worse.

Gruesome   Indicative that one has increased in height.

Guacamole   An animal that tunnels in avocado pears.

Guarantee   A sure-fire cuppa.

Guerilla warfare   A battle between two troops of monkeys.

Guidance   A social gathering at which Boy Scouts hope to get lucky.

Guide dog   A poodle that's just been promoted from the Brownies.

Guillotine   A French chopping centre.

Guise   The masculine of Gals.

Language spoken by

Gum Arabic   A Sheik who cannot find his false teeth.

Gumboots   Shoes worn over the teeth.

Gun dog   A poodle armed with a .45 revolver.

Gymkhana   (Scots) Indicative that James is unable to do the task allocated to him.

Gymnastics   Small, athletic bugs.

F

Face lift   To pick someone up by the ears.
Fait Accompli   (French) Indicating that the garden party is over.
False arrest   The wrong arm of the law.
Fanatic   Someone addicted to fans.
Fascist   Anyone who disagrees with a left-wing politician.
Fast-food restaurant   A place that specializes in second helpings.

Fat   The result of exceeding the food limit.
Fat cow   An animal with a fodder complex.
Father fixation   A priest who's glued to the spot.
Fear of flying   A bird with vertigo.
Feather-brained   Someone who is feeling down in the mouth.
Feedback   To be sick.
Felon   Dropped on from above.
Fete   A party for sportsmen – athlete's fete.
Fetish   Being in a holiday mood.
Fez   A hat worn by Helen of Troy, hence the fez that launched a thousand ships.
Fjord   A car made in Norway.
Figment of the imagination   A fruity thought.

Figure conscious   Descriptive of a brilliant mathematician.

Figurehead   A mathematical genius.

Film buff   Someone who goes to the cinema in the nude.

Finland   A country where the people are constantly on a diet.

Fire-eater   Someone with a hot temper.

Fire fighter   Anyone who takes his or her dismissal to an Industrial Tribunal.

Fire fly   An insect with arson on its mind.

Fireproof   Descriptive of your employer's relations.

First aid kit   A cat that works for the St. John Ambulance Brigade.

First class male   A boy baby that is delivered the day after conception.

Fishcake   A piece of cod that passeth all understanding.

Fish supper   Ant's eggs.

Fissure   A man who sells fish.

Flair   (Scots) The lower part of a room, usually covered by carpet.

Flame proof   Evidence of arson.

Flaming row   A blazing canoe.

Flapjack   A lumberman in a panic.

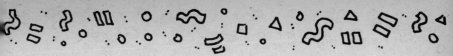

Flattery   Living in a tower block.

Flea market   The place where bugs do their shopping.

Fleet-footed   Someone who stands on sailors.

Flight of fancy   A seat in the first-class compartment of a jumbo jet.

Flippant   An insect that won't take things seriously.

Floating voter   Someone who wants to elect a Tory wet.

Floor manager   A senior carpet salesman.

Florist   A budding businessman.

Flowers   Lazy plants always found in beds.

Fly by night   1. A mosquito that comes out as soon as you put the light out.   **2**. The mode of travel preferred by insomniacs.

Flying buttress   A dairy maid on a jumbo jet.

Flying colours   The Red Arrows.

Flying doctor   A paramedic.

Flying picket   A striker who has won his wings.

Flysheet   An insect's bedding.

Flymo   Mower power to your elbow.

Foible   A story with a moral. eg. Aesop's Foibles.

Food, to bolt one's   To tie one's lunch to the floor.

Foolscap   A paper hat worn by a dunce.

Football   A game for gentlemen played for barbarians.

Football fan   A device for cooling footballs.

Footballer   Someone who gets a kick out of his job.

Footlights   Luminous toe-nail varnish.

Footman   An extremely small servant.

Forensic   To be ill overseas.

Foreshortened   IV

Forger   Someone who writes wrongs.

Forthcoming   Being placed just behind the third man in a race.

Fortitude   Life after 39.

Foul language   The way barnyard birds communicate with each other.

Franchise operation   High-street surgery.

Francophile   What Frenchmen use to clean and shape their nails.

Fragrant   A pleasant smelling instinct.

Frankenstein   A man who takes a long time to make friends.

Freebooter   An amateur soccer player.

French loaf   What Parisians do when they are not working.

Friar   The cook in a monastry.

Fringe benefit   A free haircut.

Frog in the throat   Something that's hard to swallow.

Frogman   Someone who rarely does what he's toad.

WHAT SHALL HE DO WITH THE DRUNKEN ADMIRAL!

Full Nelson   A drunken eighteenth-century admiral.
Full time   The period between a very large supper and going to bed.
Funambulist   A member of the St John Ambulance brigade with a sense of humour.
Fundamental   To back a lunatic in a sponsored swim.
Funeral director   Someone whose films are dead boring.
Furbish   A very small fir tree.
Furlong   (Scots) A request to know the length of a guest's stay. eg. You here furlong?

E

Early warning   A polite way of saying 'Do that again and I'll thump you.'
Earwig   A hairpiece with a built-in hearing aid.
Eavesdropper   Adam.
Eclipse   What a hairdresser does when cutting hair.
Egalitarianism   Eagle worship.
Egg   Something that is not beaten unless it's good.

Egg plant   A chicken factory.

Egocentric   A very peculiar chicken.

Egoism   The study of the hatching process.

Egoist   Someone who is always me-deep in conversation.

Electric chair   A device for shocking condemned men out of their bad habits.

Escort Agency   A male-order business.

Electronic bug   A fly in a fuse box.

Elliptical   The feel of a kiss.

Emperor penguin   The king of the chocolate biscuits.

Emulate   A dead Australian bird.

Engineers   The 'earing apparatus of engines.

Equator   A menagerie lion that runs round the earth.

Eskimo   One of God's frozen people.

Estimate   (French) To point out a friend.

Eureka   An unsubtle hint that someone needs a bath.

Euthanasia   Minors of China and other neighbouring countries.

Even-minded   Someone with a flat head.

Excretory   Someone who used to live in Crete and who supports Mrs Thatcher.

Exit   Old-fashioned; on the way out.

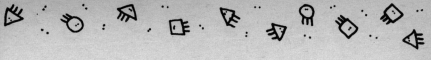

Exorcise   What ghost hunters do in the gym.
Expectant   A pregnant insect.
Explain   The most basic way of cooking eggs.
Eye-opener   A loud alarm clock.
Eye-witness   To notice that one has been winked at.

D

Dace   Plural of day, thus happy dace are here again.
Dadaism   Excessive affection for one's father.
Daguerreotype   A picture of a small knife.
Dandelion   A well-dressed big cat.
Danish pastry   A tart with a heart of gold.
Daylight robbery   The night we put the clock back.
Dead centre   An unpopular youth club.
Dead certainty   A deceased racehorse on which a large amount of money had been staked.
Deadly nightshade   A lamp cover with murder on its mind.
Dead ringer   A deceased Avon lady.
Death's door   The entrance to a funeral parlour.

Debate   Something to lure de fish.

Decadent   A ten-year-old.

Decanter   A thirst aid kit.

Deceit   A piece of furniture with four legs and a padded platform.

Declutch   De pedal between de brake and de accelerator.

Decoke   De drink dat is.

Decompression chamber   A room in hospital in which old compresses are removed.

Debark   The noise made by de dog.

Defamatory   To slander Mrs Thatcher.   *a right wing politician*

Defeat   De things dat stick out at de end of your legs.

Defence   De man criminals sell their loot to.

Definition   The state of being hard of hearing.

Defrosted hamburgers   The fry that came in from the cold.

Deign   Someone from Deignmark.

Delegate   The ambassador from the Bronx.

Democracy   A country ruled by the CND.

Denial   The main river in Egypt.

Depart   De role an actor from the Bronx auditions for.

Depressant   A downcast insect.

Derange   A Victorian cooker.

Descant   Oy yes, dey can.

Designer stubble   An excuse for being too mean to buy a new razor.

Despair   An extra tyre.

Despotic   A tyrannical insect.

Detergent   To prevent a man from doing as he wishes.

Detest   To fail an exam.

Dethrone   To knock someone off a w.c.

Devotee   Someone who is addicted to elevenses.

Dialect   A Welsh member of parliament.

Diatribe   What Ancient Britons did with wode.

Dictatorship   A sailing vessel used by Stalin.

Diet   To keep within feed limits.

Diffident   Unlike.

Digital watch   A timepiece for those who like that sort of ting.

Dik   A crazy mixed-up kid.   *a backward child*

Dilate   To telephone someone after midnight.

Dilute   To take a lute from a lute player.

Diploma   The tradesman who fixes burst pipes.

Diplomat   1. A very discreet carpet.   2. Someone who lies in state.

Dipsomaniac   Someone who is addicted to swimming.

Dirty double-crosser   Someone who sails from Dover to Calais and back again without taking a shower.

Dirty habit   The reason for a nun's BO.

Dirty joke   Something that should be obscene and not heard.

Disarm . . .   . . . as opposed to dat arm.

Disc jockey   A sportsman who rides into the record book.

Disguise   Oneself, as in 'Disguise in love with you.'

Dislexia   An inalibity to spell.

Distemper   The whiting on the wall.

Distinctive   To make a bee's home smell fresh.

Dlihc   A backward child.

Doggone   Lassie's last words.

Dogma   A young puppy's mother.

Dogmatic   A pet that takes itself for walks.

Doleful   Descriptive of a busy job-centre.

Dolphins   Barbie's water wings.

Doner kebab   Someone who agrees to give his kebabs to another person after his death.

Doodle bug   A graffiti-writing fly.

Double bass   Twins with very deep voices.

Double take   Descriptive of a busy kleptomaniac.

Down in the mouth   The result of kissing a feather-brained person.

Down-market   A place where buyers meet cellars.

Down payment   The money demanded for a duvet.

Downwards   Hospital rooms located in the basement.

Dragonfly   An insect that annoyed and subsequently was slain by Saint George.

Draw   A struggle between a dentist and his patients.

Drawing room   A dentist's surgery.

Dressed to kill   Descriptive of an executioner in uniform.

Dressing room   A storage room for mayonnaise, thousand island and other salad accompaniments.

Drill sergeant   An army dentist.

Drip-dry   A wimp with an umbrella.

Drip proof   Evidence that someone is wet behind the ears.

Drizzle   A drip that's going steady.

Dry cleaner   A thirsty refuse collector.

Duckling   A short swim.

Dublin   Increasing by the same amount again.

Dumb Blonde   *Perfide Albino.*

Dumbbells   A covey of thick beauties.

Dutch kissing   Two-lips from Amsterdam.

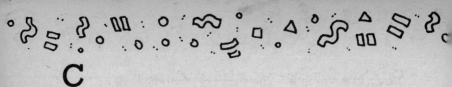

C

Cacti A prickly pear.
Cachet A tiny story of hidden money.
Caddie A young lout.

Caesar salad A command to remove a dieter's lunch from the table.
Cainamotpelk Someone who walks into shops backwards and puts things on the shelves.
Calf love A fixation about legs.
Call-to-arms An invitation to a person of the opposite sex for an embrace.
Calves Animals that follow your every step.
Camaraderie A feeling of friendship experienced by photographers.
Camel 1. A horse designed by a committee. 2. An animal that gives its rider the hump.
Camphor (Scots) The reason for attending a social gathering. eg. I camphor tea.
Campanologist Someone with good in*tent*ions.
Campsite Larry Grayson in swimming trunks.
Campus A group of boy scouts on holiday.

Cannibal   Someone who is fed up with people.
Cannon fodder   A clergyman's lunch.
Capital offence   A crime committed in London.
Capital punishment   How a Glaswegian views a day-trip to Edinburgh.
Capsize   The measurement of a hat.
Carbuncle   The automobile driven by your father's brother.
Card sharp   An ace razor.
Carnivore   Someone who eats automobiles.
Carpenter   Someone who sprays automobiles.
Carpet   Floor covering sold by the yard and worn by the foot.
Carpet salesman   A rug addict.

Cartridge   The outcome of a love affair between a partridge and an automobile.
Catacomb   A feline grooming device.
Car vacuum   A little sucker.
Catalogue   A list of pet shops.
Catatonic   A pick-me-up for depressed cats.
Catkin   Pussy's immediate family.

Cattery A room with a meow.

Cauliflower ears A medical condition brought about by attending too many lectures on the benefits of vegetarianism.

Celery What people in Glasgow and Edinburgh work for.

Census How mother knows we're around without actually seeing us.

Chain smoke To inhale the fumes of smouldering metal links.

Change of mind A drop in the notion.

Charge account An electricity bill.

Charlady A female pyromaniac.

Checkmate To ascertain the whereabouts of one's spouse.

Cheetah A big cat you can't trust.

Chef Someone who is at home on the range.

Chest of drawers A box full of knickers.

Chianti A request to do something. eg. Chianti go to the cinema tonight.

Chop chop Two karate experts shaking hands.

Christmas crackers An opinion expressed by Eberneezer Scrooge.

Church bells The vicar's most attractive daughters.

Cigarette A paper tube filled with tobacco and smoked by a fool.

Civil servant A very polite domestic.

Clairvoyant A small insect with extrasensory perception.

Claustrophobia Fear of Christmas.

Clock-watcher Someone who constantly admires himself in the mirror.

Club footed Having a foot in both camps – the Boy Scouts and the Girl Guides.

Cobra An undergarment worn by female Siamese twins.

Coconut Someone who is addicted to chocolate bars.

Cock-a-hoop A chicken crawling round a croquet lawn.

Cockerel An alarm cluck.

Coffin An expellation of air brought about by congested lungs.

Coincide What you should do when it starts to rain.

Cold comfort   An aspirin taken to relieve a cough and runny nose.

Cold-shouldered   Having icicles in the armpits.

Cold war   A snowball fight.

Collywobbles   Twins born to a male sheepdog and a packet of jelly crystals.

Colour blind   Descriptive of someone who is badly-read and never sees blue jokes.

Comeuppance   A request to visit. eg. Comeuppance me some time.

Commentator   A very vulgar spud.

Commissar   A Russian king with socialist leanings.

Common market   An economic union of European states in which snobbish Englishmen would never be seen.

Commonplace   A meeting place for vulgar people.

Communist   Anyone who disagrees with a right-wing politician.

Compere . . .   . . . com fils.

Computer dating   Taking computer friendliness too far.

GIVE US A KISS, HUNKY!

Concert programme   The promise of sings to come.
Concur   To swindle a mad dog.
Condominium   A safe house.
Conductor   A man who is always facing the music.
Conjunctivitis   The eyes have it.

Connoisseur   A man who knows a lot about drains.
Consonant   An insect that knows its ps and qs.
Consumer protection   Protective clothing worn by shop assistants in Harrods on the first day of the sale.
Consumer society   A ladies' lunch club.
Contrite   Being unable to hold a pen or pencil.
Convex   An angry jailbird.
Convince   To trick a boy named Vincent.
Cookery book   A volume full of stirring chapters.
Coq au vin   Rhode Island Red Wine.
Coq d'or   The entrance to a French rooster's house.
Cord   Cloth worn by piano players.
Corneal graft   Sight for sore eyes.
Corned beef   A load of old bull.
Corporal punishment   1. Instant whip.   2. The chastisement of NCOs.
Corporation tax   Payment made to the government by those who have excessively fat stomachs.

Corpulant   A very fat insect.

Count   The man a socially ambitious woman is out for.

Counterirritant   A fussy shopper.

Counterspy   A store detective.

Countess   A female arithmetic teacher.

Coup de grâce   To mow the lawn.

Cowslip   A heifer's mouth.

Crab apple   A fruit with two pincers found on the seashore.

Crèche   A collision between two cars in Scotland.

Crew cut   To make half the ship's complement redundant.

Cricket bat   A flying mammal found at Lord's and the Oval.

Crockery   A hospital for broken-down cars.

Crooked   An affectionate diminutive for criminals called Edward.

Crossbow   An angry curtain call.

Crossbowmen   Angry men with ribbons in their hair.

Cross-examination   1. Trial by fury.   2. A religious knowledge test.

Cross-eyes   A medical condition brought about by playing noughts and crosses too often.

Crosswort   A small plant with black and white square leaves.

Crowbar   A meeting place for alcoholic birds.
Crude oil   Liquid carbon that gushes from the ground shouting 'Knickers!'
Crustacean   Someone who likes stale bread.

Cudgel   A cow's favourite pudding.
Curtail   The prolongation of the lower spine of a dog.
Cut-throat competition   A race between two barbers ending in a close shave.
Cyclamates   Hell's Angels.
Cyclone   A bicyclist with BO.
Cyclones   Twins on BMXs.

B

B. Mus.   To confuse, musically.

Babble   A flock of very noisy sheep.

Baby   An infant human on whom a little talcum is always welcome.

Bachelor   A male who never mrs anyone.

Back down   A duck's tail feathers.

Backgammon   To bet on a pig.

Backward   A hospital room where those with spinal problems are treated.

Bacteria   A coffee shop for bugs.

Bad drivers   Everyone else on the motorway.

Badinage   A grandparent who becomes more and more ill-tempered the older he gets.

Baggage   A device for measuring bags.

Baited breath   Having a mouthful of maggots.

Baked ham   A bad actor in a stew.

Baker   Someone who works because he kneads the dough.

Baldness   Hair today; gone tomorrow.

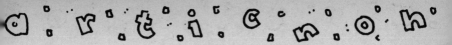

Ball cock   A soccer-playing barnyard bird.

Ballyhoo   The cast list for a performance of *The Nutcracker*.

Baltic   A spherical clock.

Bambino   Words often used by a young deer's mother.

Banana   1. A handy fruit.   2. To prohibit girls called Ana from entering the country.

Banana republic   1. A country ruled by bananas.   2. A country populated by all the Anas prohibited from entering other countries.

Bandicoot   A bald bird with bow-legs.

Bank holiday   What it is whenever your mum or dad needs to cash a cheque.

Bank robber   A thief with the gift of the grab.

Banker   A professional man who rarely loses interest in his job.

Banker's card   A cheque mate.

Bankrupt   Someone who can pay attention and nothing else.

Bank statement   Black humour for well-red people.

Banshee   To refuse entry to Australian girls.

Bantam   To refuse entry to men from Scotland.

Bantu   To prohibit the use of familiar French.

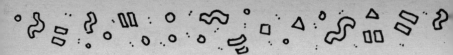

Baptism   The art of cooking bread rolls.

Baptism by fire   To be christened in hot water.

Barbarian   A pub striptease artist.

Barbary ape   Someone who does an impression of a man's hairdresser.

Barber's pole   A hairdresser's assistant born in or around Warsaw.

Barber's shop   A clip joint.

Barefaced   Having the appearance of Paddington or Yogi.

Barefaced liar   A mendacious person with no facial hair.

Barmen   What feminists would like to do.

Barnacle goose   A member of the anserine family with extremely bad acne.

Barnstorm   Raining agricultural buildings.

Barometer   An instrument that measures how often a wheelbarrow has been used.

Baron of beef   A rich butcher knighted by the Queen.

Baseball   A social gathering for the wrong sort of people.

Bashful   A very busy party.

Bass clef   A musical fish.

Bath bun   A very clean sponge.

Bathing belle   A girl worth wading for.

Battalion   1. A division in the vampire's army.   2. A game of cricket in which lions are used instead of balls.

Battering ram   A sheep used to break down doors.

Battery farming   Rearing portable electrical cells.

Battery hen   An electric chicken.

Battle-axe   A domineering woman used as a weapon by medieval soldiers.

Battle royal   A domestic dispute involving the Queen and the Princess of Wales.

Bawdy house   A dwelling, the road to which is paved with rude intentions.

Beachcomber   1. A hairdresser who specializes in cutting the hair of sandy-haired customers.   2. A hairdresser who works at the seaside.

Beanstalk   The language of Heinz.

Bear baiting   Putting a grizzly on the line.

Bear hunt   To search for a nudist.

Bear witness   A large animal that gives evidence in court.

Beatitudes   Young members of the beat generation.

Beautician   A khol-miner's daughter.

Beauty spot   A place where attractive girls gather.

Bed   (Polite Scots) Naughty.

Bed bug   A listening device placed under the pillow.

Bed of roses   A prickly but sweet-smelling place to sleep.

Bedsitter   A paid employee who looks after baby beds when mummy and daddy beds are out.

Bedspread   A lavish feast taken in a four-poster.

Bedstead   A four-poster ridden in the Grand National.

Beck   (Polite Scots) Where the tradesman's entrance is.

Beef tea   Feeding time on a ranch.

Beefeater   A warder at the Tower of London with a penchant for Big Macs.

Beehive   (Cockney) An order to calm down. eg. Beehive yourself.

Beeswing   1. An insect that plays in a jazz band.
2. A playground entertainment for young insects.

Beforehand One less than befivehand.

Beggar my neighbour Living next door to a gypsy camp.

Begonia A warning to leave. eg. Begonia big cissy.

Beguine To start to perform a South American dance.

Behindhand Knuckles, fingernails and the other parts of the back of the nether upper limbs.

Belisha beacon A flashing pig that can't spell.

Bell-bottoms Self-ringing trousers.

Bellboy A young lad who bangs his head against the belfry.

Benign What you are for the year before your tenth birthday.

Beret The fruit of any plant worn on the head.

Best man A male attendant at a wedding who doesn't get the chance to prove it.

Bewilder To behave in a much worse manner than before.

Bezique A card game that makes you throw up.

Bias To bid farewell to a young donkey.

Biathlete To purchase Daley Thompson.

Bidet D-Day minus two.

Bigamist 1. A heavy Italian fog. 2. Someone who has loved two well. 3. Someone who has been found out doing what many would like to get away with given half a chance.

Big game hunter Someone looking for a giant set of *Trivial Pursuit*.

Bigotry An Irish oak.

Bird of passage A pigeon trapped in a corridor.

Bird of prey A religious canary.

Bison To purchase a brother for your daughter.

Bitter end A bum who blames everyone else for his misfortune.

Black comedy A dirty joke.

Black eye The result of having come into contact with a guided muscle.

Black humour A sikh joke.

Black magic A conjurer from Africa.

Blancmange A dandruff-like disease that affects dogs.

Blasted heath How Mrs Thatcher views her predecessor as leader of the Conservative Party.

Blind ambition A guide dog with dreams of winning the Greyhound Derby.

Blind date   A romance between two Venetians.
Blind infatuation   A hedgehog in love with a cactus.
Blind Man's Buff   The skin of a sightless person.
Blinded by science   The unfortunate result of an accident with a bunsen burner.
Blitz   A congregation of Bachelors of Literature.
Blockhead   Someone who is really square.
Blood bank   A vampire's larder.
Blood count   A vampire's arithmetic lesson.
Blood money   A vampire's bar bill.
Bloodthirsty   Descriptive of a vampire in the desert.

Bloomers   Loose undergarments that flower once a year.
Bluebottle   An insect that tells rude jokes.
Blue chip   A piece of potato left in the fridge too long.
Blueprint   A dirty postcard.
Blunderbuss   A coach being driven up the wrong lane on a motorway.
Boatswain   (Scots) The offspring of a sailing vessel.
Bobby-dazzler   A policeman with a very bright torch.
Bodyguard   A tight corset.
Bog oak   A tree that grows in the lavatory.

Bojangle   A foppish male who wears too much jewellery.

Bollard   An over-inflated soccer ball.

Bombard   A lousy playwright.

Bombe Alaska   Russia's revenge for a US attack on Moscow.

Bombshell   1. A self-destructing egg.   2. The place where naughty bombs are sent to after they die.

Boo-boo   Twin ghosts.

Book of Common Prayer   The working class Bible.

Bookworm   A well-read crawler.

Boomerang   A chorus of disapproval for a collapsed pudding.

Bootstrap   A device for catching escaped shoes.

Borax   A sharp-headed hand tool used to drill for oil.

Bore   Someone who can't even entertain a thought.

Bottomless pit   A glutton's stomach.

Boundary   A home for ill-mannered men.

Bouyant   The opposite of a girl ant.

Boycott   The bed your baby brother sleeps in.

Boyhood   A twelve-year-old juvenile delinquent.

Bow-legged   Someone who uses his lower limbs to play a stringed instrument.

Bowmen   Males with ribbons in their hair.

Braise   The first words in a religious cannibal's cookbook. eg. Braise the lord for he is tender.

Brahman   A man in drag.

Brandish   The bowl you eat your breakfast cereal in.

Bravery   A wigwam set aside for young Indians.

Breathless   An under-developed female.

Bricklayer   The result of putting a chicken on a diet of cement.

Brocade   Assistance for famine-stricken badgers.

Broderie anglaise   A proper sew and sew.

Brouhaha   A happy drink.

Bruise   To make black and blue tea.

Buck-toothed   (American) Descriptive of someone who puts his money where his mouth is.

Bucket shop   The place to buy airline tickets at prices you don't pale at.

Budding genius   An expert gardener.

Bureaucracy   A country ruled by desks.

Bully off   A playground tyrant with BO.

Burst pipes   Descriptive of a broken organ.

Bushel A shrub that grows from bulbs, everyone having hidden their light under it.

Bus conductor An offensive travel official who constantly tells his customers where to get off.

Busy Lizzie A plant that refuses to mind its own business.

Butterfingered Descriptive of someone who Storks with his hands.

Butterfly An insect that thinks it's a goat.

Byre A room with a moo.

A

A Levels Exams taken by Cockney horses.

Aardvark Effort. eg. 'Aardvark will get you through exams.'

Abbreviate Descriptive of a French cheese popular in Britain.

Aberrant An insect that rarely does what it's told.

Abominable Snowman An Eskimo with a bad temper.

Aboriginal The very first able-bodied seaman.

Absinthe   That which makes the heart grow fonder.

Absolute zero   The reward for handing in a blank exam paper with a spelling mistake in your name, and the wrong date on top.

Abundance   A *thé dansant* with no liquid refreshment.

Academy   A place of learning for ill-mannered boys.

Acarpous   A furry toy animal with a mobile head placed on the rear window ledge of a car and popular with those who like that sort of thing.

Accent   Something you don't have yourself but which people from other parts of the country have.

Accident   An unfortunate occurrence regarded by your parents as deliberate.

Accolade   A fizzy drink made from the fruit of the Accola tree.

Accommodate   To insert small curved marks between words to indicate a pause.

Accomplice   Used by parents to describe your best friend.

Accomplish   A fellow alcoholic.

Accordian   A portable musical instrument made by a macramé enthusiast.

Accountants   Upright people who rarely lose their balance.

Accrue   To gather together increasing numbers of sailors.

Accumulate   A question asked by a Yorkshire schoolmaster of pupils who turn up at 10.00 am.

Accuracy   A small house set aside for a curate.

Ace   Frozen water found in posh parts of Edinburgh.

Acerbity   A tiny piece of a knight.

Acetate   An expression used by London tour guides when pointing out a major art gallery.

Aching void   Descriptive of the mouth after an extraction at the dentist's.

Acne   A rage we all go through.

'Acne carriage   A spotty taxi.

Aconite   A trainee swindler.

Acorn   In a nutshell, an oak.

Acoustic   (Scottish) A crutch for an injured heifer.

Acquaintance   Someone you know well enough to borrow from but not well enough to lend to.

Acquainted   An old-fashioned newspaper boss.
Acre   A tooth that hurts.
Acrophobia   Fear of 5,240 square yards.
Acropolis   Uniformed guards who police an area of 5,240 square yards each.
Across   Something we all have to bear.
Adage   To claim to be older than one actually is.
Adam and Eve   A dis-Abeled family.

Adam's apple   Something that's hard to swallow.
Addict   Someone who can't stop doing sums.
Add insult to injury   To call a man with a broken leg a fool.
Adhesive tape   A sticky cassette.
Administer   The government official in charge of publicity.
Ad nauseum   Sickness brought on by over-exposure to television commercials.
Adolesence   The stage between doing what you are told to and doing what you want to.
Adultery   The stage between adolescence and death.

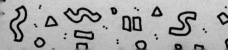

Adversity   Where television commercial directors learn their trade.

Aerofoil   The silver wrapping around a bar of chocolate.

Aftermath   The break between a geometry lesson and an English class.

Again and again   To double the profit.

Age   Something that disproves the maxim that what goes up must come down.

Aggrandize   To transform an upright piano into a grand one.

Agony column   The queue in a dentist's waiting room.

Agoraphobia   An abnormal fear of blood.

Agrophobia   Fear of farmers.

Airspace   A bald patch.

Alarm clock   A device that scares the living daylights into you.

Alimony   The cost of leaving.

Allied   A confession that one has not told the truth.

Alliteration   The act of scattering little bits of paper on the pavement.

Allocate   A form of greeting used when talking to girls called Catherine.

Aloe   A word often used by a policeman. eg. 'Aloe! Aloe! Aloe!'

Alphabet soup   A meal that makes you eat your own words.

Ambiguity   The ability to get round the truth without telling a lie.

Ambrosia   Our Fodder which art in Heaven.

Ammonia   The first word of an old music hall song, 'Ammonia bird in a gilded cage.'

Amphibians   A confession by more than one person that a lie has been told.

Amphora   The age of an Italian girl just before her fifth birthday.

Amputee   Someone who is cut short in his prime.

Animal cracker   A lion-tamer's whip.

Anode   An electrifying piece of poetry.

Antagonize   To make your aunt disappear.

Antediluvian A Frenchman who was opposed to the building of a famous Parisian art gallery.

Antelope 1 Advice given by a mean grandfather to one of his unmarried daughters. 2 Either of your parent's sisters who walks in a curious way.

Anticlockwise A female relation who is constantly looking at her watch.

Antifreeze A female relation locked in the fridge.

Antimatter Fondness for one of your female relations.

Antimony An inheritance from a female relative.

Antipasta An Italian on a diet.

Antipathy Not caring for your female relations.

Antique 1. A very old insect. 2. Something your grandmother threw out years ago and now wishes she hadn't.

Aperitif A set of dentures.

Aphrodisiac An accountant from Africa suffering from vertigo.

Apiculture An ape who can play *The Moonlight Sonata*.

Aplomb What Jack Horner pulled out of his pie.

Request for | Account Information

Account Name: Mr/Mrs/Miss/Ms

Account Number (808): `2 0 9 5 6 5 6 8`

Current/Deposit Account
(Delete as applicable)

☐ Please let me know the balance of my account

☐ Please send a Statement of Account

☐ Please prepare a Statement of Account for collection

Signature _____

(This portion to be retained by Branch)

NWB1329 Rev Apr 87-1

NatWest | Account Information

The balance of your Current/Deposit Account £ _1,151.97_ credit/~~overdrawn~~

At the close of business on _____

Please remember that you can also obtain the balance of your Account at any of our SERVICETILLS - as well as obtain cash, order a statement and new cheque book.

Apologist Someone who is sorry that he volunteered for the US space programme.

Apostrophe An award given to the Mailman of the Year.

Apothecaries' weight The length of time you stand in a chemist's shop waiting for a prescription to be made up.

Appendix The part of a book that the author has found impossible to fit into the main text.

Apple-pie order Something supplied by Mr Kipling.

Apricot A bed for baby monkeys.

Arcade What Noah gave to the animals on the ark to drink.

Archaeologist Someone whose career's in ruins.

Archbishop A pointed clergyman.

Archduke A coy nobleman.

Arch enemy Someone who favours straight lines.

Arctic The clock in the ark.

Arithmetic teacher Someone who knows how to make the little things count.

Arm Something you won't come to if you are careful.

Armada The first words in the feminist's Lord's Prayer.

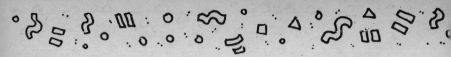

Armature Descriptive of either upper limb on an eighteen-year-old.

Armchair critic Someone who reviews armchairs.

Aroma A rootless person with BO.

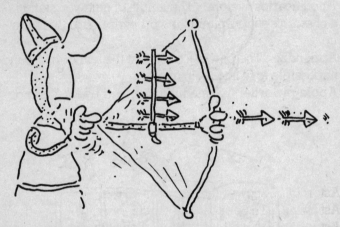

Aromatic A fast-firing bow used by medieval archers.

Arriviste Someone who ends swell.

Arrowhead The senior master at one of England's top public schools.

Art attack A severe pain in the chest brought about by over-exposure to paintings.

Artefact An expression of surprise on being told something for the first time.

Art gallery 1 The place where a transplant surgeon hangs organs removed from one patient before stitching them into another. 2 A hall of frame.

Artless The state of being between transplant operations.

Aspersion A donkey from Persia.

Assail A sick donkey.

Assegai An assertion that the person one is looking at is male.

Asset A small donkey.

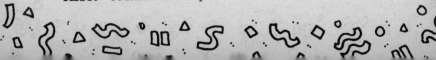

Asset stripper   A small donkey that insists on taking its clothes off.

Asteroid   A flower that grows in space.

Astronaut   The opposite of astrois.

Astringent   A well-brought-up man with a sharp tongue.

At a loose end   Descriptive of a frustrated knitter.

At death's door   Sitting outside a funeral parlour.

Atlas   An expression of relief. eg 'Atlas, we're done.'

Atoll   The landing fee one is charged before being allowed on a small coral island.

Attaché case   A diplomat's coffin.

Attitude   An article of headgear of moth-eaten appearance.

Auctioneers   The hearing organs of someone who sells things.

Autobiography   A self-writing car.

Autocracy   A state governed by motor cars.

Autocue   A billiards stick that works for itself.

Automat   A self-cleaning carpet.

Automatic data processing   A computerized marriage bureau.

Autosuggestion   A hint by one's wife that she wants a new car.

Avarice   An alternative to chips suggested by an Italian waiter.

Aversion therapy   A method of suppressing an undesirable habit by learning poetry by heart.

Aviary   Home Tweet Home

Aye-aye   An animal that always agrees with you.

Azure   An acceptance of a proposal of marriage.